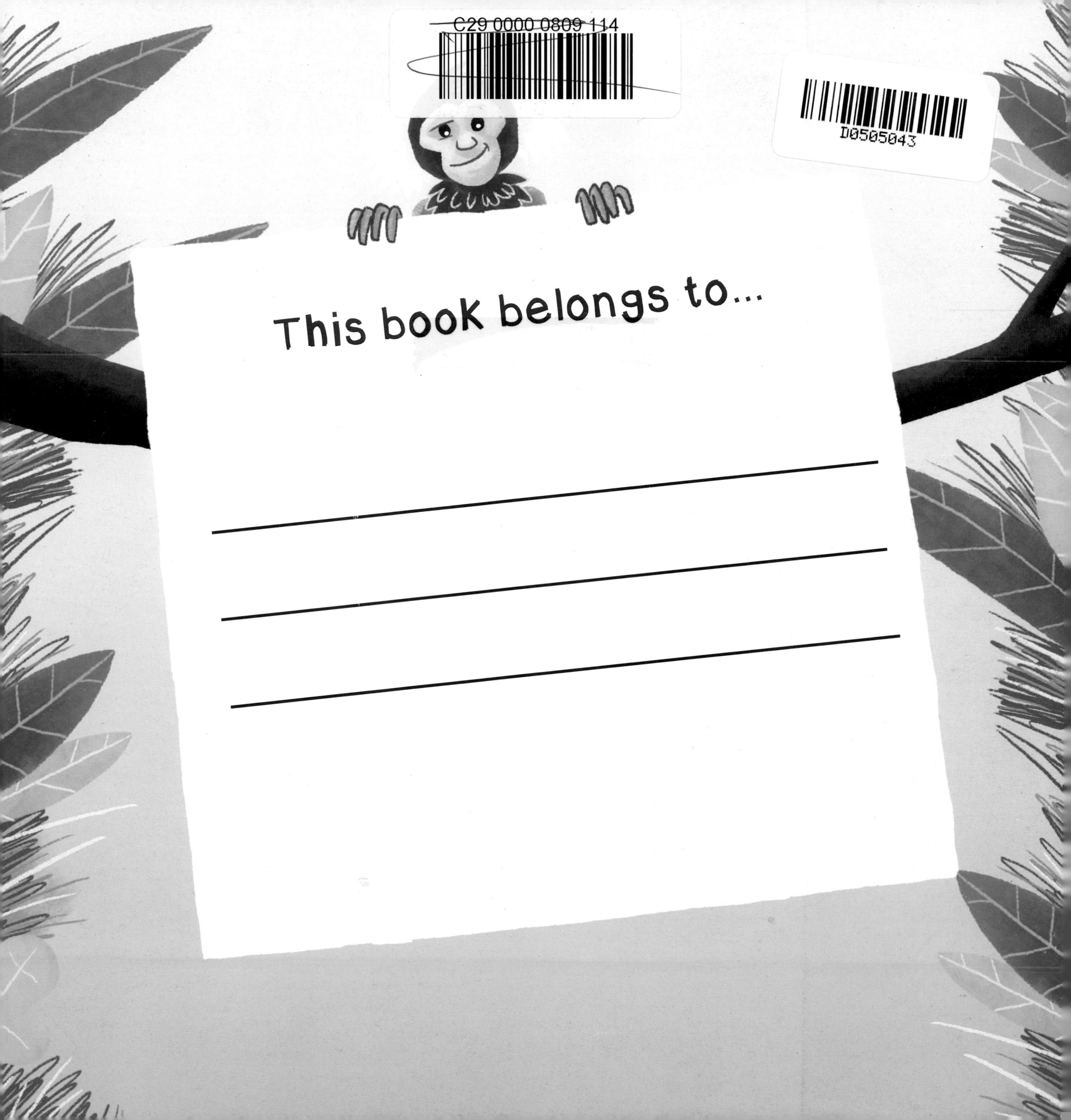
This book belongs to...

***Iguanas Love Bananas***
An original concept by authors Jennie & Chris Cladingbee

Illustrated by Jeff Crowther

MAVERICK ARTS PUBLISHING LTD
Studio 11, City Business Centre, 6 Brighton Road, Horsham,
West Sussex, RH13 5BB, +44 (0)1403 256941

Published October 2019

A CIP catalogue record for this book is available at the British Library.

**ISBN 978-1-84886-430-6**

Maverick publishing
www.maverickbooks.co.uk

# IGUANAS LOVE BANANAS

Written by
Jennie & Chris Cladingbee

Illustrated by
Jeff Crowther

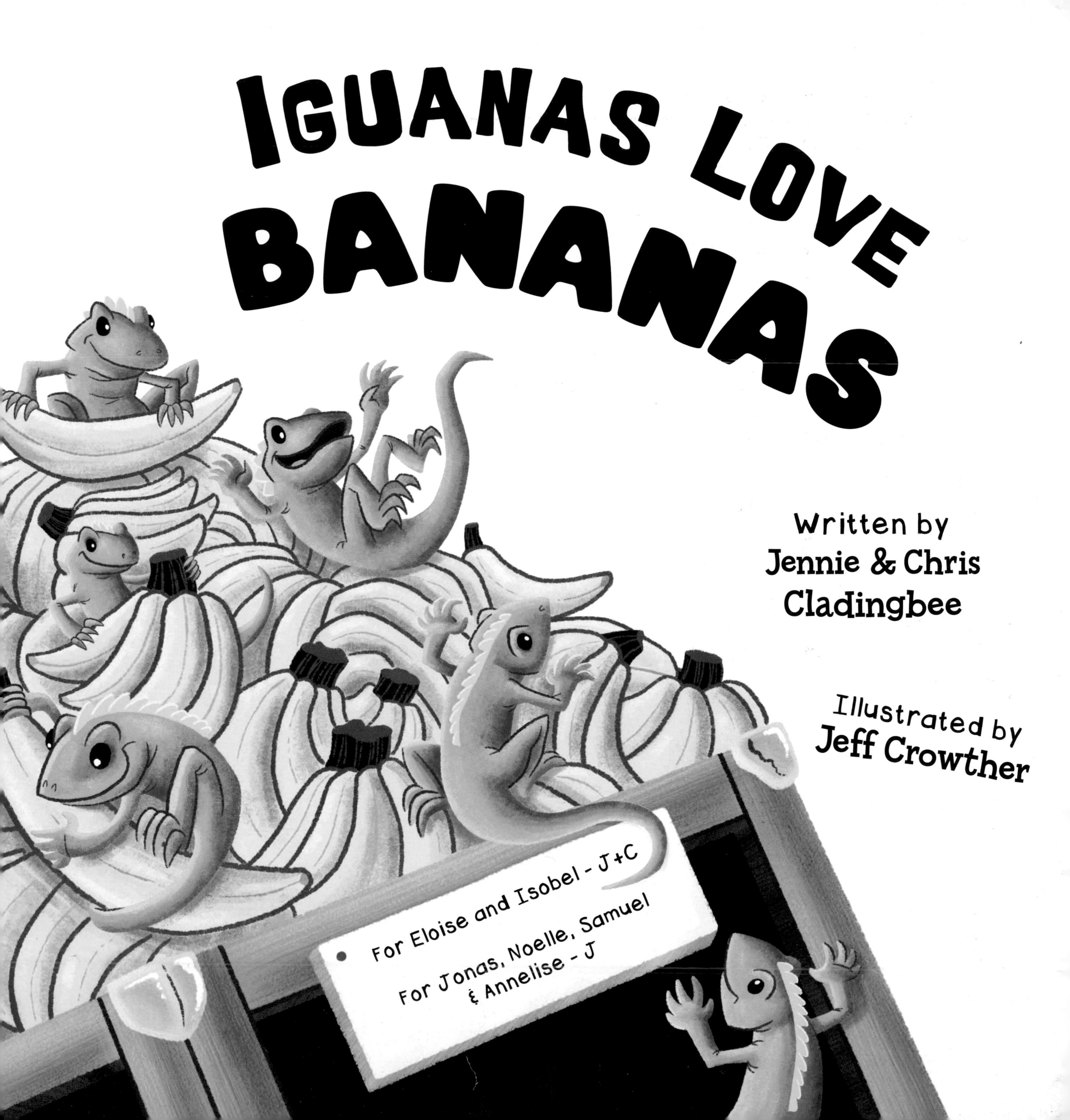

Who Knew?

**Iguanas** love **bananas**,

though they find them hard to peel.

**Cheetahs** like **fajitas**,

as they make a speedy meal.

Cockatiels like jellied eels,
though some would think this funny.
MENU
JELLIED EELS

**Alpacas** like **cream crackers**, which they dip in jam and honey.

**Albatross** scoff **candy floss**,

but then get sticky feathers.

**Koala bears** eat **chocolate éclairs**,

at rowdy get-togethers.

ÉCLAIRS
KOALAS

**Water voles** like **sausage rolls**,
but **bees** prefer **cream teas**.

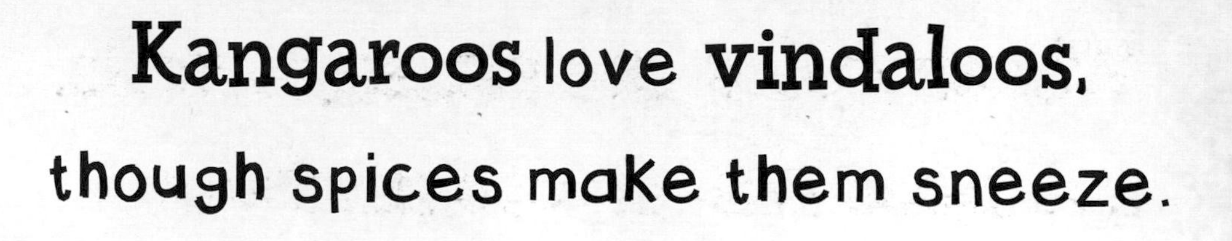

**Kangaroos** love **vindaloos,**

though spices make them sneeze.

**Chimpanzees** like **mushy peas**,

**baboons** like **macaroons**.

**Manta rays** like **crème brûlées**,

they crack the tops with spoons.

**Mountain goats** eat **porridge oats,**

for warmth in wintry weather.

**Newts** like **fruits**

and **bamboo shoots**...

....but **never** both together.

**Jaguar** like **caviar**, it's so sophisticated!

**Manatees** love **strong blue cheese**,
but get quite constipated.

**Marmosets** love **stuffed courgettes,**
they always ask for more.

Alaskan moose like apple juice,
they slurp it through a straw.

Tufted puffins eat blueberry muffins,

while hiding in their holes.

Though **parrots**

don't mind **carrots**,

they prefer **profiteroles**.

**Rats** and **mice** like **sticky rice**,
all folded in a leaf.

**Guinea pigs** like **roasted figs**,
but pips stick in their teeth.

**Elephant seals** like **microwave meals**...

....and **poodles** like **pot noodles**.

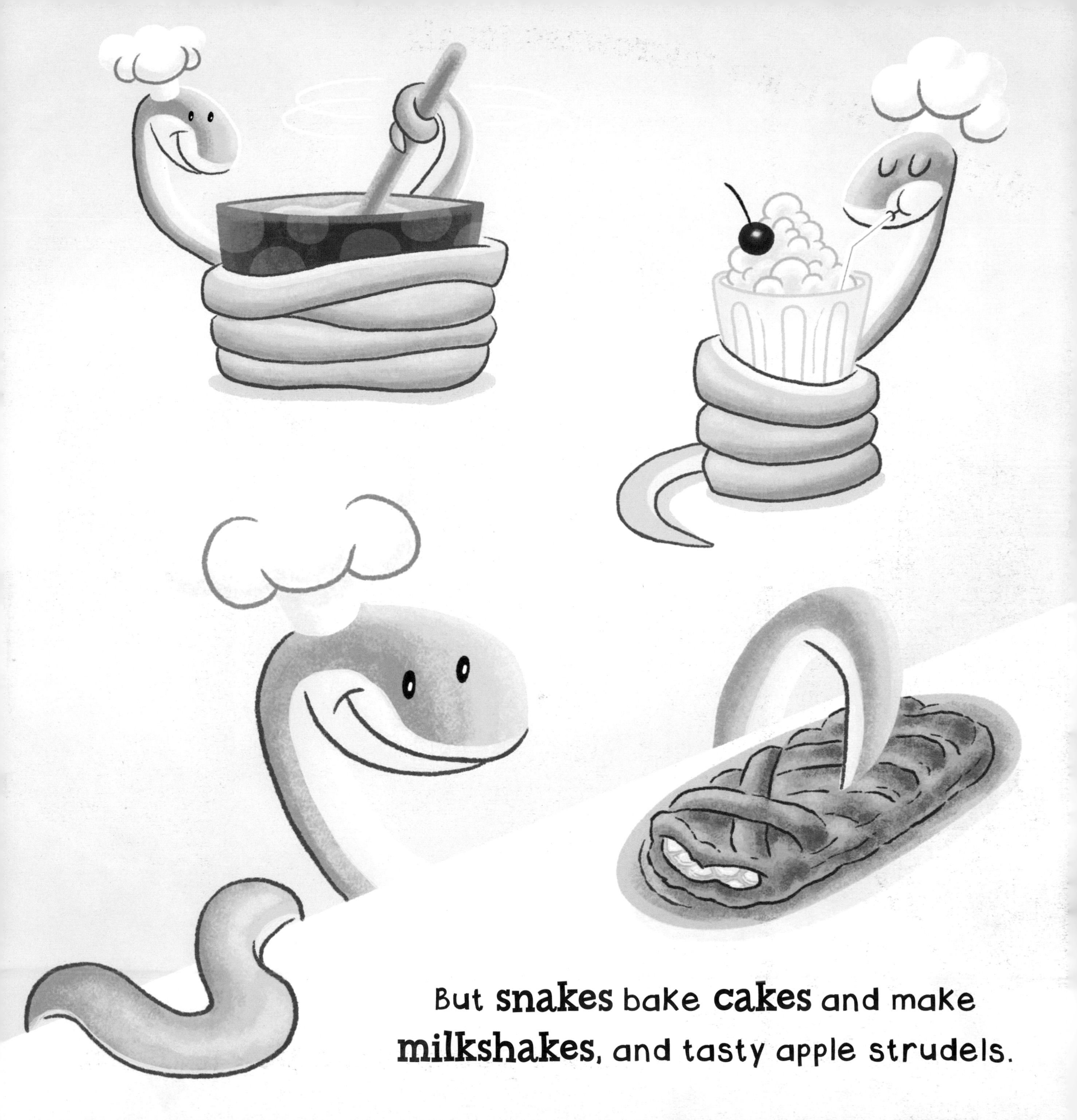

But **snakes** bake **cakes** and make **milkshakes**, and tasty apple strudels.

Plenty of pets like potato croquettes,

but others have their doubts.

All sorts of **beasts** love **festive feasts**, but...

...**NO ONE** likes Brussels sprouts!

(Well, almost no one!)
Mmmm... yum!